REA

John Snow

80003527692

First published 2013 by
A & C Black, an imprint of Bloomsbury Publishing Plc
50 Bedford Square, London, WC1B 3DP

www.bloomsbury.com

Copyright © 2013 A & C Black
Text copyright © 2013 Jack Challoner

The right of Jack Challoner to be identified as the author
of this work has been asserted by him in accordance with
the Copyrights, Designs and Patents Act 1988.

ISBN 978-1-4081-7840-9

A CIP catalogue for this book is available from the British Library.

All rights reserved. No part of this publication may be
reproduced in any form or by any means – graphic, electronic or
mechanical, including photocopying, recording, taping or information
storage and retrieval systems – without the prior permission
in writing of the publishers.

Printed and bound by CPI Group (UK) Ltd, Croydon CR0 4YY

1 3 5 7 9 10 8 6 4 2

MIX
Paper from
responsible sources
FSC
www.fsc.org
FSC® C020471

REAL LIVES

John Snow

Jack Challoner

A & C BLACK
AN IMPRINT OF BLOOMSBURY
LONDON   NEW DELHI   NEW YORK   SYDNEY

Dedicated to all those people
still suffering and dying needlessly
from easily preventable diseases,
and to all budding scientists and politicians
prepared to do something about it.

Northamptonshire Libraries & Information Service	
80 003 527 692	
Peters	13-Feb-2017
920SNO	£5.99

Contents

1
Cholera

1832, Killingworth, near Newcastle upon Tyne

'Mr Snow, come quick – it's me sister!'

The boy was hurtling down the main road of Killingworth village. His voice echoed off the grey stone buildings and leaked up and out into the dusk, dissolving into an evening that was already filled with despair.

John Snow could hear the urgency in the boy's cries. He picked up his medical bag quickly, but with a heavy heart. It was only his third day in the village, but he had already attended several patients with the disease that everyone was dreading.

'It's the cholera, I know it is. Please, can you come and see, can you help us?' The boy, about nine years old, stood in front of John, bent over, hands on his knees, the words forced out between his panting breaths.

John recognised the boy; the previous day, he had tended to the boy's father, whom he had diagnosed with cholera – and who had since suffered a painful and tormented death. 'Let's go,' he said with an upward nod, and the two of them walked briskly side by side back up the main street, without saying a word.

It was August 1832. John Snow was only nineteen years old, an apprentice doctor who was tending single-handedly to the five hundred or so inhabitants of the coal-mining village of Killingworth. His master, William Hardcastle, was back in Newcastle upon Tyne, about six miles to the south, where cholera had already claimed hundreds of lives in the past year. The disease had stalled in February, but it had recently begun claiming lives once again, in Newcastle and in Killingworth – so Hardcastle had had no choice but to send John to Killingworth on his own.

There had been nine cases of cholera in Killingworth in January and February, five of them fatal. John was determined to give people the best care and treatment he could, to minimise the number of cases now that the disease had returned there.

They turned off the high street, still walking at a brisk pace. John and the boy both flinched when they heard an explosion at the coal mine; using gunpowder to loosen the coal from the coalface had become common practice in the past few years. John pictured the people working in the mine – boys as young as five dragging and pushing trucks loaded with coal up through cramped tunnels; men hacking at the coalface or shovelling up loosened coal from the floor. Workers typically stayed in the mine for ten hours at a time, not even coming to the surface to go to the toilet – despite the fact that of course there were no lavatories inside the mine.

Stepping into the house, John saw the boy's younger sister laid out on a bed next to the fireplace. The dim flickering of firelight and candlelight made the little girl's gaunt face look even more ghastly. Her eyes were shadowed and deep-set, her skin wrinkled like a prune, her face in a tortured spasm. She was flailing to and fro in agony, her breath more laboured than her brother's had been after running headlong down the high street. In a husky voice not much more than a whisper she was asking for water; her mother was trying to give her some from an earthenware jug, but most of it was spilling onto the bedclothes as the girl writhed around in pain.

John took a candle from the mantelpiece and knelt beside the girl to take a closer look. He glanced at the mother, not knowing what to say – he was a man of few words even at the best of times. Still, he was conscientious and took his job very seriously. He knew what to look for – and he knew, too, that there was little he would be able to do.

The girl's skin was cold and clammy, her pulse hardly present. She was frothing at the mouth and John could see her tongue, white and flaccid. She had a cut on her arm – probably the result of her violent thrashing movements – but her blood was black and treacle-thick and was hardly flowing at all. All the signs were there – this was cholera, without question.

Suddenly, diarrhoea exploded onto the bedclothes, already wet with the same. But it wasn't brown: instead, it was thin and murky grey. Doctors referred to this product of cholera as 'rice water'.

'Please, do something,' the mother blurted out through her tears. 'I can't lose *her* as well, I just can't!' The woman's desperation and utter sadness cut through John. He felt her pain, but he stayed calm. He rubbed the girl's arms and legs vigorously, which brought blood briefly back into them. But, despite the low light, he could see the flesh quickly return to its blue-grey colour. Some people referred to cholera as 'the blue death', because of the distinctive change in a victim's skin tone.

'Do you have more blankets?' John enquired, as he opened his bag, looking for laudanum, a painkiller made from opium that was the best doctors could give to ease sufferers' discomfort. 'We need to keep her warm.'

His voice became a mumble, as he began addressing himself: 'Camphorated oil... calomel... a hot poultice...' He sighed, knowing it would probably be for nothing.

'She is at an advanced stage of the disease,' John said calmly, out loud now. 'Why didn't you fetch me earlier?'

'Me boy has only just got back from the mine – he's been working all day – and I've been dealing with me husband. They took him away and I just followed them – I didn't know what else to do. He didn't even get a proper burial. They just chucked him in the ground, and not even in the churchyard.' She was agitated, and distraught, her watery eyes reflecting the candle flame. 'We only just come home.'

'You know I ought to have your daughter moved out,' John said, thinking of the government's advice to move cholera patients to a designated hospital. But he could see the anguish in the mother's face, and didn't want to upset her further – or have her shout at him. So nothing more was said about moving the girl, and the room remained horribly quiet for a while, except for the gentle whooshing of the coal fire in the grate and the increasingly laboured breathing of the patient. But if you could hear doom, the sound would have been deafening.

Time passed; there was more rice-water diarrhoea, more anguish, more frothing at the mouth – but no sign of any improvement.

At around ten o'clock, the mother told her son to go to bed – he would still have to go to work at four the next morning. John knew that the boy's wages, pitifully small though they were, would be even more important now that his father had died. Women were not allowed in the mine, and there was little other work around. Perhaps the mother might be able to get a job working as a maid for one of the mine owners, or maybe even the great George Stephenson, who also lived in the village. Mr Stephenson was an engineer, and his powerful, chugging steam engines helped haul the trucks out of the mine.

Lost in thought, John was jolted back to reality – not by noise, but by the lack of it. The woman's daughter had stopped flailing around, her breathing had become very faint, and she had slipped into unconsciousness amid the bedclothes drenched in vomit and diarrhoea.

The woman knelt and prayed to God to save her daughter, and John wondered how she would cope with the sadness of losing another member of her family. He wondered, too, how this disease could take hold of someone so quickly, and without a fever, and how it could kill so horrifically. What was going on inside the victim's body? Why was there so much watery diarrhoea? Why did victims' blood turn thick and black? And was there any way to cure the disease – or, better, stop it spreading?

Soon afterwards – despite John's best efforts and despite the prayers – the girl was dead.

2
A Sharp Intake of Breath

21st October 1848, Soho, London

John Snow was half asleep – or was it half awake? His head felt heavy against the back of his chair. He had just been breathing in chloroform, a gas that makes people become unconscious and can be used as an general anaesthetic. He felt dizzy and not quite all there. The experience was pleasant and uncomfortable at the same time. But he was used to it.

It was a cool October evening in 1848 – sixteen years after John had faced cholera in Killingworth. He was sitting alone in his home in Soho, in London, gazing out of the window at the deep yellow sky, the evening clouds illuminated by the setting sun. The golden backdrop silhouetted the building opposite, and created a lingering green after-image whenever he closed his eyes. For a moment, he kept his eyes shut and watched the after-images dance, and he drifted a little further from consciousness.

In this dream-like state, John began thinking back to his younger days as an apprentice – and in particular, his experiences of cholera. He pictured himself back in Killingworth, and remembered that poor girl and her mother. And he couldn't help letting his mind wander over and pick up the same old questions.

How did cholera spread? How did it affect the body? No one knew the answers, but John had recently hit upon a new idea, and he was excited about it.

People had been dying from cholera for hundreds, if not thousands of years, unknown to most of the world. Until 1817, the disease was confined to a small part of India, around where the River Ganges empties into the Bay of Bengal. In that region, the disease was endemic, which meant there were about the same number of cases each year. But in 1817, it became an epidemic: there were many more cases than usual. And over the next few years, it turned into a pandemic, spreading across a much wider area. It burst out of India and expanded across much of the rest of Asia, killing many hundreds of thousands of people. Some people called it 'Asiatic cholera', to distinguish it from an ordinary bad case of diarrhoea, which had often been referred to as cholera. Officially, this new disease was known as 'cholera morbus'.

In 1823, that first pandemic's fearful roar mysteriously shrank to a whisper. But four years later, cholera rose up and spread again, this second pandemic radiating out from India as before, but reaching even further. Into Russia. Into Europe. It even crossed the Atlantic Ocean to America. And in October 1831 it reached Britain.

The first cases in Britain were in Sunderland, about twenty kilometres from Newcastle upon Tyne, where John was training at the time. Over the next few months, cholera spread to many parts of the country. Altogether, the epidemic claimed well over fifty thousand lives in Britain. Then, towards the end of 1832, the epidemic died away almost as quickly as it had come – and now, in 1848, there had been no cases in Britain for sixteen years.

John had pulled that train of events through his mind many times – each time, stopping it to wonder about what this terrible disease really might be and to see if the new idea he had had could explain how it spread. The bright golden glow from outside caught his eye again, and he realised his thoughts had wandered away from the task at hand. After all, he wasn't breathing in chloroform for fun. He was supposed to be doing an experiment: working out how much chloroform would be a safe and effective dose to give to people who were about to be made unconscious before having an operation.

Now aged thirty-six, John Snow had been fully qualified for ten years, having left his family home in York in 1836 and studied in London for two years. He was based at his home – an apartment in 54 Frith Street. He went out to see patients, he did small operations, and he prescribed medicines. Dr Snow had also made a name for himself as an anaesthetist. Two years earlier, in 1846, he had studied the first general anaesthetic – a gas called ether. Patients would take a deep breath of ether vapour and go to sleep. But at first, the results had been unreliable. Sometimes people only stayed asleep for a few minutes and woke up in the middle of their operations, in absolute agony. Sometimes, people slept for hours after their operation was finished. And sometimes, people simply died from having inhaled too much ether.

John had investigated ether, in a makeshift laboratory in his home. He kept a variety of animals on which to test the vapour before testing it himself – although he took care of the animals, and only used them when necessary. He had designed a device, an inhaler, that enabled anaesthetists to give accurate doses. And he had written a book explaining the effects of ether, how to make your own ether inhaler and how to administer it for the best results.

His services as an anaesthetist were now as much in demand as his skills as a doctor. Most days, he would visit hospitals and put several people to sleep before they had their teeth pulled, their appendix removed or perhaps a leg or an arm amputated. Often he would take his apparatus to people's houses; some people preferred to be put to sleep and cut open in the comfort of their own homes.

He was making enough money to survive in London, and he had gained a good reputation among his patients and other doctors. But he wasn't interested in becoming rich or famous. He was more interested in solving mysteries, in finding truth; John was as much a scientist and a philosopher as a practising doctor and anaesthetist. His mind was always wandering, picking up questions and searching for possible answers. Now he was working with this new anaesthetic, chloroform, to do what he had done for ether: finding out how to administer the perfect dose.

As he took another breath of the vapour, John's mind turned once again to cholera. No one had much idea of what the disease actually was, let alone how to cure it. But most doctors and scientists were agreed on one thing: they believed that cholera was caused by a kind of noxious gas or vapour called miasma. The source of the miasma, they supposed, was decaying food, dead animals, or anything else filthy or rotting. It seemed to make sense, because cholera was more common in dirty, cramped places, where lots of people and their waste lived in close quarters. If you breathed in the miasma, you would develop cholera.

The idea of bad air causing disease was not new: another disease, malaria, had even been named after the Italian words for 'bad air' (*mala aria*). The connection between dirt and disease seemed certain, and most people took it for granted that disease was caused by miasma.

But John didn't believe that people caught cholera by breathing in miasma. His big idea was that the cholera 'poison' entered the body not via the lungs, but by being swallowed. Exactly what the poison was he didn't know, but he was convinced of its source: the rice-water diarrhoea of a person with the disease.

Of course, no one would swallow diarrhoea on purpose; but the cholera poison in the diarrhoea could find its way into the water supply – when the drenched sheets from a person's sick bed were washed, for example, or when sewers overflowed, their contents leaking into wells. Or perhaps the hands of a person treating the patient or touching the bedclothes might pick up the poison; if that person then prepared a meal, the food would be a perfect vehicle to carry the poison into someone's digestive system.

Another, grander, thought struck him: the sewers, which carried the diarrhoea of thousands of cholera victims, flowed into rivers – the very rivers from which many people got their drinking water!

John was convinced his idea was right, but knew that it would be hard to prove it, and even harder to convince other doctors and scientists. To most of them, the idea that people caught cholera by breathing in miasma was the one thing about the disease of which they were certain.

Cholera hung there in his mind, like the after-image of the sunlit sky lingering in his eyes. There was a good reason why the disease was occupying John's mind now: although Britain had been free of cholera since 1832, the disease had recently returned. The thought of it filled him with dread.

As he sat there, turning it all over in his mind, he noticed that the golden sky was slowly turning darker and redder, but now he could hear raindrops tapping the window. A storm was coming.

John sat up in his seat, feeling a little more level-headed. That was good, because he had to get ready for a meeting later that evening. He pushed the thoughts of cholera away and lifted himself up out of his chair.

An hour later, John was putting on his greatcoat and opening the door of 54 Frith Street to set off for the meeting.

3
Return of the Blue Death

It was only a ten-minute walk to the house where the Westminster Medical Society met. As he turned into Savile Row, John glanced at his pocket watch. A quarter to eight; plenty of time.

The front door of number 17 was open, allowing a little light from the warm gas lamps out into the cool night. John could see that the hallway was quite crowded.

He would normally have shuddered a little at the thought of entering a room full of people chatting; he had always been a bit shy when talking to people he didn't know very well. But this was different. The people inside that hallway, and in the meeting room, were all doctors, just like him. And they all had an interest in learning and discovering more about their profession, just like him.

Besides, he had been a member of this society for ten years now. He had given several presentations on subjects he had been researching, including ether and chloroform; he was on the Society's committee, and had recently been made one of its vice presidents. He felt very much at home here.

'John! Good evening,' one man said, shaking John's hand the moment he stepped inside. It was Dr Garrod.

'Alfred – it's good to see you again.' John smiled, shaking his umbrella dry just outside the door. It was hard to fold down, with its whalebone struts.

Dr Alfred Garrod and John had both recently been lecturing at the same medical school. And they had something else in common: they both shared an interest in discovering the truth about cholera. John smiled as he imagined explaining his new ideas to his friend. But he wasn't ready to discuss his theory with anyone – not even Dr Garrod, not quite yet. Besides, there wasn't time: the meeting would be starting in a few minutes.

There were about sixty members and guests crammed inside the meeting room, and John wasn't the only one whose head was filled with thoughts of cholera. The return of the disease to Britain during the summer, and now to London a couple of weeks ago, had nudged it to the front of people's minds. Most of the doctors in that room had witnessed the terrifying symptoms of cholera first-hand, and no one wanted a return to the horrors of the disease's last visit. And yet, doctors had made little or no progress in understanding the disease, let alone treating it effectively.

The President of the Society, John Webster, stood at the front of the room and waited patiently until everyone was ready. 'Good evening,' he offered after a moment. 'Welcome to the first of another season of meetings of the Westminster Medical Society.'

Dr Webster was upbeat. During his opening speech, he mentioned John Snow's book about ether, which had been published the previous year. A murmur of respect bubbled through the room, and John looked around and smiled.

Dr Webster went on to discuss cholera, but he tried to allay people's fears about the disease.

He suggested that another disease – scarlet fever, or scarlatina – was a much greater threat. Nearly one thousand people had died from scarlatina in London alone, in the six weeks before the meeting, far more than from cholera. And he had something else to say:

'I think scarlatina deserves as much attention as cholera – especially because it usually attacks children and young people; cholera, on the other hand, generally affects drunkards and persons of worn-out constitutions.'

John cringed a little at Dr Webster's comment. Although he, too, believed strongly that alcohol was an evil in society, he didn't think that being drunk made you more likely to catch cholera. *What gives you cholera*, he thought, *is swallowing the cholera poison that has come out of someone else's backside – not drinking alcohol.* However, Dr Webster was right about the fact that scarlet fever had killed many more people than cholera in the past few months. Perhaps this new cholera epidemic would die away before it became too serious.

After Dr Webster's speech, another member of the Society, Dr Hird, spoke about his experiences with cholera patients, and suggested several remedies. 'I have attended many patients suffering with the cholera: the blue, wrinkled skin; the watery diarrhoea; the torment.' He went to describe the symptoms in great detail, and how he had also carried out twelve *post mortem* examinations on cholera victims – cutting up their bodies to find out why they died.

Eventually, Dr Hird detailed his approach to treating the disease. 'Unfortunately, there is no known medicine or treatment that can deal with the specific cholera poison. All we can do is try to stop the diarrhoea and give the patient as much strength as possible so that they can resist the influence of the poison. When the disease is in its early stages, I suggest giving compound chalk powder – that is chalk with cinnamon, powdered tormentil root and a little opium.'

John knew that Dr Hird's advice was based on his experience – but he couldn't help thinking it would be next to worthless. What did doctors really know about the disease? If you don't know how a disease is caused, how can you possibly find an effective treatment? Besides, John had begun to think that prevention would be better than cure. If he was right about cholera poison being swallowed, people could take simple precautions to avoid catching the disease: drinking filtered or boiled water; and washing their hands after touching a cholera patient or their bedclothes.

John also began to have another thought – something he hadn't really considered before. The only way cholera could become a pandemic was if the cholera poison reproduced, made more of itself. If there were only a fixed amount of the poison, the disease would never have affected more than a few people; it would have become extremely diluted very quickly. But millions of people had had the disease.

'How can a poison reproduce?' he mumbled beneath his breath. 'Perhaps it causes the intestines to make more of it once it's inside – some kind of chemical reaction. Or what if it is not a chemical, but a living thing?' He knew that there are worms that live in people's intestines, and that they reproduce there, making millions where there had only been a few to start with. And those worms can only get inside the intestines in one way: by being swallowed. Perhaps the cholera poison was something similar.

Dr Hird was still talking: 'In the later stages of the disease, when rice-water diarrhoea has begun, the best course of action is this: first, a mustard emetic,' (something to make the patient throw up) 'followed by a few grains of acetate of lead, opium and spirit of cinnamon every half hour, and an enema of starch, turpentine and laudanum.' (An enema involves flushing liquid up the rectum with a special syringe.) 'It is important, too, to rub a hot mustard poultice on the chest and arms, to stimulate breathing and circulation.'

After Dr Hird was finished, several other doctors took turns to recount their experiences of the disease. John was one of them. He spoke about the shortness of breath cholera victims suffer, and how it was caused by the slowed-down circulation of the thickened blood. Thick, slow blood can't carry oxygen efficiently around the body, so the brain increases the breathing rate, desperate for more oxygen.

While he was speaking, he felt a tremendous urge to proclaim his theory, there and then. It seemed the perfect moment. But no. Convincing the medical profession that people caught cholera by swallowing poison that had come from someone else's intestines – and not by breathing bad air – would be a tough job. It was an extraordinary claim, which meant it would need extraordinary evidence. And now John needed to find some.

4
Evidence

August 1849, London

Ten months after that meeting at the Westminster Medical Society, on a sweltering sunny Saturday morning, John was on his way to Horsleydown, near to the south bank of the River Thames. It was a part of London where people lived in cramped, dirty conditions – and, apparently, it smelt bad, too, so it had been no surprise to the government's Board of Health or the Commission for Sewers that a cholera outbreak had occurred there. After all, it was bad smells that spread the disease, wasn't it?

John had read about the outbreak in the newspaper, and he had also studied a report written by John Grant, assistant surveyor for the Commission of Sewers. Now he wanted to visit the location for himself, to see if he could find out how the victims had caught the disease, and if it would give more support to his theory. Over the past few months, he had been reading scientific reports, writing to the Board of Health, and talking to doctors and to people who had lost family members. Everything seemed to support his idea that people caught cholera by swallowing its 'poison', and not by breathing foul air.

At ten o'clock, he stood at the north end of Waterloo Bridge. The rattle of stagecoaches and horse-drawn buses on the cobbles mingled with the calls of street sellers in the sultry air. There was a bonneted elderly woman with a large wooden tray full of apples, two men selling oysters from a wooden bucket on a table, and a girl sitting down with a basket of vegetables.

'Apples! Ha'penny a dozen!' 'Penny a lot the oysters!' 'Last vegetables this side of the river! Ooh, sir, you look like a real gentleman. Need something for lunch?'

John had already bought food for his lunch, after taking a slight detour to the market in Drury Lane, so he walked past without saying a word. He paid the toll of half a penny and pushed through the turnstiles. He stopped halfway across the bridge to see how the builders were getting on with the construction of the Palace of Westminster – what most people refer to as the Houses of Parliament. The original buildings had been destroyed by fire more than fifteen years earlier, and it was still mostly a burnt-out ruin when John had arrived in London thirteen years earlier. Now, the new buildings were nearing completion, and John thought they looked splendid. Most exciting was the huge clock tower, more than half built, which would one day reach over three hundred feet into the air and have four huge clock faces and loud bells chiming on the hour and half-hour. John could imagine that it might become one of the most recognisable landmarks in the city.

Smoke from a thousand factories hugged the skyline; steam ferries and working boats chugged along the river. John could see people walking along the muddy river bank below, picking out whatever they could find that might be worth anything: pieces of metal, lengths of rope, scraps of fabric. The smell rising up from the river was disgusting, especially on such a hot day and when the tide was low. It was no surprise: all the waste and filth from the streets and houses floated down drains, through sewers and into the river at several places. The worst smell came from human excrement.

The sewers carried a lot more waste now than they used to. Over two million people now lived in London, most of them scraping a living however they could. In the majority of homes, where often several people lived in a single room, the toilet would be a small building outside, called the privy. In fact, the privy would normally be shared by the occupants of several houses. Their urine and excrement would drop into a cesspit underneath.

Years before, the cesspits had been emptied regularly, in the middle of the night, by people who would take the contents out of the city and sell it for use in compost. But these days, that happened more rarely, and most cesspits were overflowing, the rainwater washing their contents down the drains. And in recent years, Mr Chadwick, the head of the Commission of Sewers, had recommended the building of more sewers, so that the waste –

and the bad smells – could be taken away from where people lived and into the river.

Most people also had a bucket or a chamber pot that they used in their homes, and which was afterwards emptied into a drain outside. So most of the human waste ended up in the drains, then the sewers and ultimately the river. As John gazed down at the filthy river, he wondered whether cholera poison recently ejected from people's intestines was also there, floating among the other detritus.

What was certain was that thousands of people had this very water supplied to their homes, and that there was a connection between the water supply and cholera. John had written to all the water companies that supplied water to the pumps in the neighbourhoods and homes of London. He had also scoured the records of deaths from cholera in different districts of London over the last year.

He had discovered that of the 7,466 deaths from cholera in the capital, nearly six thousand were in the south and east of London; inhabitants of those districts were over three times more likely to have died than those in other parts of the city.

The main difference, as far as he could see, was that the people in the worst-hit areas were supplied with water taken from the most polluted parts of the river.

He had also studied the records of cholera deaths from other towns and cities around the country, and found that cholera always seemed to be most widespread and devastating in places where the water supply was taken from the rivers into which the sewers emptied.

John was satisfied that his research into the water companies added weight to his theory. But he still needed more evidence.

The reason he was venturing south of the river today was that the outbreak that had happened there a couple of weeks earlier had affected the people in one set of buildings much more than the people in another set of buildings just across the road. There were more than thirty cases of cholera, and eleven deaths, in Surrey Buildings, but just two cases, with one death, in Truscott's Court. The number in Truscott's Court was about normal – but why were there so many cases in Surrey Buildings? Mr Grant's report had described the toilet facilities and water supplies of the two groups of people. John wanted to see it for himself.

He arrived at Thomas Street, in Horsleydown well before lunchtime. He mumbled to himself as he made notes of what he found, so that he could write up his observations later.

'... two courtyards, close together, consisting of a number of small houses or cottages. Inhabited by poor people ...'

'... in Surrey Buildings, slops of dirty water poured down by the inhabitants into a channel in front of the houses got into the well from which they obtained their water ...'

'... some of the rice-water diarrhoea from the first victims must have become mixed with the water people drank, since a number of additional cases occurred almost simultaneously ...'

He bit his lip as he scribbled furiously. A man standing nearby watched John wandering slowly around the courtyards, examining the privies and the drains and the water pumps and taking notes. 'Excuse me,' the man piped up eventually.

'Good day,' John offered, looking up only briefly from his notebook.

'Are you Dr Snow?' the man enquired. 'I'm Mr Russell.'

It was the doctor who had attended the first cases of cholera in Surrey Buildings.

'Ah, Mr Russell!' John gave the man his full attention now. 'Good of you to come.'

John asked Mr Russell to tell him anything he had noticed about the cholera patients – and in particular, he asked about the bed linen:

'Do you know if the fouled bedclothes of the cholera patients were washed?'

'Yes. Some were washed while I was there, in buckets. Afterwards, the contents were poured into that channel over there.'

The doctor pointed to the channel that John had been looking at – the one whose contents could easily leak into the well from which the people of Surrey Buildings took their water. John Snow was almost ready to go public with his idea.

5

Communication

29th August 1849, London

John sat at his desk, summer sunlight pouring in once again through the casement window. In front of him were piles of paper. All of the evidence he had collected seemed to support his theory, and now he was putting the finishing touches to a short book in which he explained his theory and set out the case for it.

'You've been there all day, sir,' his housekeeper noted. 'You'll strain your eyes. Can I get you something to eat? Some water? Distilled, of course.'

John had been in the habit of drinking distilled water – boiled to make steam and then cooled back to liquid again – ever since he read a book that suggested clean water and a vegetarian diet would guarantee good health. And now that he had become convinced that some diseases pass from one person to another through drinking water, he was more keen than ever on the ultra-pure, clean water. He had installed a device for making distilled water in the kitchen. The housekeeper had objected at first, but now she was quite used to operating it, and would often take some of the water home for her family.

'Yes. Thank you, Alice.' He stood, just to stretch his arms and legs, and opened his jaws in a wide yawn. Through the window he watched a horse and cart pass by along Frith Street below.

He thought back to his conversation with Mr Russell in Horsleydown a couple of weeks earlier. As it happened, Mr Russell had also attended the very first cases of cholera in London in the current epidemic, nearly a year earlier, which had also been in Horsleydown. So of course, John had asked him about that, too.

The first victim had been a sailor called John Harnold, who had just arrived from Hamburg, in Germany, where cholera was rife. Mr Russell's words were still clear in his mind:

'On 22nd September, Harnold rented a room, developed all the classic symptoms of cholera, and was dead within a few hours. A few days later, another man, a Mr Blenkinsopp, rented the same room – and he, too, died from the disease.'

If cholera was carried by a miasma – by bad air – and if that air had been hanging around that area at that time, there would surely have been other cases of the disease nearby. But there were no other cases in the area at the time, only the two in the same room a few days apart.

It seemed beyond doubt that Blenkinsopp had caught the disease from Harnold; the cholera poison from Harnold's diarrhoea must have been present somewhere in the room. In other words, the disease was *communicated* from Harnold to Blenkinsopp.

Ah, that's a good word for the title of the book, thought John. '*Communication*'.

John turned from the window and sat back at his desk. He read back over his account of another visit he had made recently, to the site of another outbreak. It was even more striking, and held even better evidence.

This time it was a row of houses in Albion Terrace, Battersea. Once again, he had initially read a report about the water supply and the sewers, by the same John Grant who had written the report on Surrey Buildings. Over a period of just two weeks, there had been around fifty cases of cholera and twenty-four cholera deaths among the hundred or so inhabitants of Albion Terrace. But there were no other cases in any other houses nearby.

To John, the single most striking fact was that all the houses shared the same water supply. Albion Terrace was not in a poor area: these were well-to-do middle class people – professionals. They weren't living in squalor, nor were they drunkards. Each house had its own privy, behind the house.

But, Mr Grant had found, the cesspits underneath the privies were close to tanks that held water ready to be drawn by pumps in the kitchens. And, crucially, the water tanks of all the houses were connected by an overflow pipe.

The outbreak had begun soon after heavy rain had caused blocked drains to overflow, sweeping excrement from the cesspits into the water tanks. Most of those who had not caught the disease had refused to drink the water, because it smelt and tasted foul after the heavy rainfall.

Next, he thumbed through a scientific report written by Dr Garrod, his friend from the Westminster Medical Society. He had read it several times already, and had mentioned it in his book. Dr Garrod had carried out a scientific analysis of the thick, dark blood of cholera patients. The doctor had found that the only difference between it and healthy red blood was the water content: the thick black blood was just normal blood with much less water in it. This fact tallied with John's theory. All the water expelled in the rice-water diarrhoea – often as much as twenty-five pints per day – must come from somewhere. Water would be taken from anywhere in the body, making the patient extremely thirsty and severely dehydrated, with wrinkled skin – and thick blood.

But why would the body flood the intestines with so much of its precious water? To John, the answer was simple: because it was trying to flush away the cholera poison – the poison that was in the intestines. And how did the poison get into the guts? The person swallowed it. It made perfect sense. But most other doctors still believed that the cholera poison affected the blood directly – entering the blood via the lungs when it was breathed in.

Several months earlier, John had paid a visit to Dr Garrod and another member of the Westminster Medical Society, Dr Parkes, who was also interested in cholera victims' blood. John had explained his theory to them – but both men had been sceptical.

'It doesn't make sense to me,' Dr Parkes had sneered. 'I was in India back in 1832. A couple of scientists actually tried drinking the rice-water diarrhoea, and gave it to animals to drink, to test exactly the idea you have just expounded. None developed the disease. And the washerwomen who cleaned the clothes of the sick were no more likely to get the disease than the general population. No: cholera spreads through the air. I'm sure of it.' And Dr Garrod agreed.

Nevertheless, here, in his apartment in Frith Street, John Snow was grinning. To him, it was clear: all the pieces of the puzzle seemed to fit, and he could see the whole picture. He was nearly on the last page of his book. Time to add something about prevention. He picked up his pen, paused for a moment, then wrote:

If the writer's opinions be correct, cholera might be checked and kept at bay by simple measures that would not interfere with our everyday affairs; and the enemy would be shorn of his chief terrors.'

He paused and looked up. *Hmm. 'Shorn of his chief terrors'; I like that,* he thought. He continued writing:

It would only be necessary for all persons attending to a patient to wash their hands carefully and frequently, never omitting to do so before touching food, and for everybody to avoid drinking, or using for making food, water into which drains and sewers empty themselves; or, if that cannot be accomplished, to have the water filtered and well boiled before it is used.

He paused again. 'Where's Alice with that distilled water? I'm parched,' he mumbled. He looked down again, pen in hand:

The sanitary measure most required in London is a supply of water for the south and east districts from some source quite removed from the sewers.

It wasn't the most eloquent writing, and not particularly easy to follow. But it was a fitting ending to the book that laid out, John hoped, convincing evidence that his ideas were correct.

An hour or so later, he had added a few more paragraphs to finish off, and then took great pride in writing:

FRITH STREET, SOHO

AUGUST 29TH 1849

A few days later, he took his book to a publisher nearby – and a week after that, he held in his hands a copy of his book: *On the Mode of Communication of Cholera*, by John Snow, M.D.

6

Something in the Water

13th October 1849, London

Fog mingled with smoke in the streets of London as John approached Savile Row for another meeting of the Westminster Medical Society.

It was more than a month since his book had been published, and despite all his research and his careful explanations, it seemed that few doctors were convinced by his ideas.

The most prestigious medical journal, *The Lancet*, had written that John's theory should be 'received with great limitation', and that it was 'not by any means decisive'. The Lancet's review did recommend that doctors read John's book for themselves, but it seemed that few had bothered to do so.

The sun had set less than three hours earlier, but the clear sky was allowing heat to pour out into space, and there was a distinct chill in the air. Making his way through the cold night alone, John paused for a moment to hitch up his scarf a bit higher around his neck, then walked on.

After nearly a year, in which cholera had claimed around fifty thousand lives in Britain, the current epidemic was finally slowing down, and would probably soon be over. That was good news, of course – but John couldn't help thinking that if the epidemic did weaken, and people's attention turned to other things, the medical profession would be no more prepared for the disease next time it struck than they had been this time.

At the moment, every newspaper and medical journal was stuffed full of news, views and statistics about cholera – not surprising, since several hundred people were still dying of it every month. In fact, that was probably why John's own book had been a bit overlooked – like a single voice blending into the noise in a crowded room.

A few weeks earlier, another journal, *The London Medical Gazette*, had dismissed John's book as 'a modest contribution to the medical literature on cholera'. That had hurt. The review said, 'There is, in our view, an entire failure of proof that the occurrence of any one case could be clearly and unambiguously assigned to the use of the water.'

Even the president of the Westminster Medical Society, John's good friend Dr Webster, had not given John's theory much consideration. At the previous week's meeting, Dr Webster had been discussing various theories about cholera. He had mentioned the fact that at the end of August and the first week of September, there had been a rise in cholera cases.

'This increase coincided with a particularly dry few weeks, where there was also very little atmospheric electricity – no thunderstorms,' he had said. 'In dry conditions, noxious air spreads more easily. Cholera certainly seems more prevalent near open sewers, over-stocked graveyards, crowded and unventilated places where bad air can linger.'

Rotting vegetables? Noxious air? Electricity? The same old stories – and John was convinced that none of these had anything to do with cholera. Why couldn't anyone else see that?

The negative response to his theory had left John feeling dejected. But this evening, walking through the foggy air, he had a spring in his step. There were two reasons why John was happier tonight. One was that he was about to give a presentation about his book; it would be a chance to explain his theory, in person, to other doctors. He quickened his pace. The door to number 17 was open, and the warm glow from inside beckoned as usual.

'Ah, here's Dr Snow now.' John could hear a familiar voice as he stepped into the warmth. It was Dr Webster, and he was standing next to someone John didn't recognise. Dr Webster introduced the two men. 'Dr Swayne: this is Dr Snow. John: this is Dr Swayne, from Bristol.'

Dr Swayne was the other reason why John was feeling positive. He and another Bristol doctor, Dr Brittan, had recently made a discovery that had caught the attention and imagination of the medical profession. The two doctors had been studying samples of cholera patients' diarrhoea under the microscope, and both had seen tiny cells in nearly all the samples – cells they claimed were not present in samples of diarrhoea from people who didn't have the disease.

The discovery suggested that cholera might be caused by a tiny, single-celled living thing that lived and reproduced inside the intestines. The cells had also been found in the air around cholera patients – this fact made John a bit sceptical, as it suggested that you could catch cholera by breathing in these cells, while his research had shown it was only through swallowing. Nevertheless, the new discovery had got everyone talking about the possibility that the 'cholera poison' was a living thing that thrived in the intestines and arrived there by being swallowed. That was enough to lift John's spirits.

Dr Brittan and Dr Swayne's observations had attracted much more attention than John's book. But John didn't mind – his theory had even got a mention. Another Bristol doctor, Dr Budd, used the microscope observations to form a theory similar to John's, but he gave John credit for suggesting it first. John was not experienced in using a microscope, and he hadn't even tried to see the cells that Swayne and Brittan had seen. Anyway, his theory concentrated on how cholera spread, not on what actually caused it.

A few weeks earlier, *The Lancet* and *The London Medical Gazette* had both published detailed descriptions and drawings of the cells, and the medical profession had been excited. But this week's *Gazette* contained an article by a respected London microscopist, Dr Parker, who suggested that Swayne and Brittan were mistaken. Dr Parker claimed that those cells were found everywhere, and had nothing to do with cholera.

'Is that yesterday's *Gazette*?' John said, glancing down at the paper in Dr Swayne's hand.

'Yes,' Dr Swayne pushed out through a sigh. 'Dr Parker is entitled to his opinion, but I know what I saw. And everyone seems genuinely interested in Dr Budd's ideas – and yours of course. I read your book avidly, and I, for one, think it's brilliant. I'm looking forward to your presentation, Dr Snow.'

'Thank you. Shall we go through?' John suggested.

Just before John began his presentation, he gazed around the room. It was good to see so many people – so many minds – ready to consider his ideas. There would be a chance for a discussion afterwards, too. And with Dr Swayne there, the idea that cholera was caused by something that happened inside the intestines might really be driven home. Tonight could be a turning point.

When the audience's chatter became just less than a murmur, he began, in his characteristic gruff voice:

'Writers on cholera, however much they differ in their views of the disease, generally consider it to be an affliction of the whole body, acting either on the blood or the nervous system. But in diseases in which a morbid poison has entered the blood, there are general symptoms of illness – usually a fever. That's not the case for cholera. On the contrary, the disease begins in the intestines, and often proceeds with so little feeling of general illness that the patient does not consider himself in danger until the symptoms are far advanced. I believe that cholera is, or at least starts with, an infection of the inner surface of the intestines.'

John spoke for more than an hour, reading through what was basically an updated version of his book. He had collected new evidence, from more towns and cities across Britain, and had also added in a bit about the plight of miners, who still had to endure shifts underground of eight or more hours with no toilets or fresh water.

'... In some places, the people have to use water that has been pumped out of the mines, which of course is liable to be contaminated by the miners' excrement ...'

Everyone listened intently, and John was glowing inside. After he had finished, he mentioned the discoveries of Dr Brittan and Dr Swayne, and gave a nod in Dr Swayne's direction. John admitted that the fact that the strange cells had also been found in the air had made him think twice about the new observations, because all the evidence he had gathered pointed to the fact that you get cholera by swallowing, not by breathing.

Dr Swayne stood up and spoke briefly about his observations, and showed everyone his drawings. And that was really all there was time for. There was no opportunity for a discussion – no chance to find out what everyone thought about John's ideas. That would have to wait until the following week.

Before he knew it, the meeting was over, and all the members were leaving. As he stepped out into Savile Row, the fog and smoke were even thicker.

7

Victoria

7th April 1853, London

The sun was shining as John stood in front of Buckingham Palace, the home of Britain's royal family. He was both excited and daunted by what was about to happen: he was going to meet Queen Victoria and administer chloroform, to relieve her pain during the birth of her eighth baby.

He stood for a moment, watching the top hats, bowler hats and bonnets on the heads of passers-by; the large bustled dresses on the well-to-do women; the dirty rags on the group of children now collecting up the horse manure from the street. Handcarts, horse-drawn carriages, boys offering to shine shoes for a penny a time; it all began to blur together in his mind.

Nearly four years had passed since that frustrating meeting at the Westminster Medical Society. The following week's meeting had been more disappointing still: when the Society's members finally had their chance to discuss John's presentation, he found little support for his ideas.

A Dr Sibson spoke the longest, insisting that the only thing that seemed certain was that cholera depended upon the weather. He specifically disagreed with John's ideas because, he said, some people suffered for some time before the diarrhoea started – 'so how could it be that this disease begins in the intestines?'

A Dr Bird said that the intestines are probably involved somehow, but 'that was only secondary, happening after the weakening of the blood.' Some doctors suggested that dirty water might be part of the story. But not one of them agreed with John's theory.

A few weeks after the meeting, even the excitement about the discoveries of cells in the diarrhoea had died down, turning into confusion and controversy. Other doctors had tried to repeat the observations of Dr Swayne and Dr Brittan:

they found starch granules, they found human cells that must have broken away from the lining of the intestine, they found fungus cells that were also found in flour – and in some cases, they found nothing. And, as John predicted, the medical profession really did lose interest in the disease soon after the epidemic died away, at the end of 1849.

John pushed his memories away and focussed on what he had been called to do. The Queen would probably be going into labour very soon. He glanced up at the wide front part of the building, which had only been completed a couple of years before. It looked splendid. In 1852, John had moved to a grander house on Sackville Street, not very far from his old home – but it was nothing like this, of course.

'I'm Dr Snow,' he announced confidently at the Palace Gate. 'Sir James Clark sent for me.' A guard beckoned him in.

Inside, the palace was very grand. Gold everywhere. Expensive furniture. Vast halls with wooden panels; huge doors that led to enormous rooms. Colossal oil paintings hanging on the walls.

It all made him feel very small – but also very proud, that this son of a labourer from York could be summoned here by the Queen. He had already been here once, to meet Queen Victoria's husband, Prince Albert, so he was reasonably at ease as he walked the long walk to the room where the Queen lay in the early stages of labour.

'Dr Snow, Ma'am,' the guard said with a bow. She was pleased to see him.

'Ah, Dr Snow. My doctor, Sir James, tells me the time is near – and my body agrees. I am grateful for your attendance. I have heard very good things about you.'

'An honour, your majesty.' John bowed, wondering if he was saying and doing the right things.

After a moment of awkward silence, the queen's own doctor spoke up.

'Uh, Dr Snow – if you would be so good as to wait in the annex.'

John gave a nod and walked through to the next room. He didn't speak for a while, instead taking in the splendour that was all around – even in this small annex room. There were long red velvet curtains, and a deep red rug covering most of the floor.

On a little table next to the window, there was a copy of the Bible. John thought it a little odd at first – a Bible in a room that was obviously not really used very much. But then he noticed a religious man, a bishop perhaps, sitting in the shadows in the corner.

'Good day,' John offered.

The bishop leaned forward and grinned playfully. 'You're here to take the Queen's God-given pain away,' he said.

Without the bishop's smile, John would have felt extremely uneasy. There were many religious people who believed that easing women's pain with chloroform during childbirth was morally wrong. They believed that God had made childbirth painful for women on purpose, as a punishment for Eve who had, according to the Bible, sinned in the Garden of Eden.

'Just doing my duty to the head of your Church,' John replied, with an equally playful smile.

There were two other doctors in the room as well, and they were soon joined by Sir James.

'I have no moral qualms about the use of chloroform in childbirth,' Dr Laycock mused. 'But I do think it prolongs the labour. What do you think, Dr Snow?'

'I haven't found it so,' John replied rather flatly.

'What do you think can be done to stop chloroform being used for the wrong purposes, Dr Snow?' Dr Ferguson enquired. The newspapers often featured stories about robbers, muggers, kidnappers and murderers who put their victims to sleep by covering their noses with a handkerchief soaked in chloroform. It had given the drug a bad name in recent years.

'I suppose any invention can be used for good as well as for bad,' was all John could muster. Discussions of that sort always made him feel uncomfortable, especially since anaesthesia had become his main source of income – and especially now that he was about to administer chloroform to the Queen!

Minutes later, John was called in to the room where the Queen was. She was in labour, and the painful contractions had started. John put a few drops of chloroform on a handkerchief then held the handkerchief against the Queen's nose. 'Just take a deep breath in through your nose, Ma'am.' There was enough chloroform to take away the pain but not enough to put the queen to sleep.

After less than an hour, John's work was done. The baby was coming, and was born soon afterwards. It was a boy, who was later named Leopold.

Two weeks later, the Queen wrote in her diary: 'Dr Snow administered that blessed chloroform, and the effect was soothing, quieting and delightful beyond measure.'

Leaving the palace, John was touched again by pride. He was making good money from treating wealthy patients – although he also tended to poor people, too, sometimes without charging them. He had earned respect in his profession, and had just been elected as Vice President of the Medical Society of London – the new, larger society formed when the Westminster Medical merged with another one. And now here he was, tending to the Queen.

This was the second time she had had chloroform during childbirth – the first time he had been asked for advice but had not come to the palace. He was confident that after receiving royal approval, giving birthing mothers pain relief would be controversial no more.

Along with the pride, he felt frustration. His cholera theory was invisible, redundant in a land where cholera was all but forgotten.

But a few months later, in the hot summer months, the dreaded disease reared its head once again. Another of John's predictions came true: doctors were no more prepared for cholera this time than the last.

8

A Fair Test

'Yes! Yes!' John exclaimed out loud – although only he and his new housekeeper, Jane, were in the house. Such was the delight in his voice that Jane came rushing upstairs to see what was up. John hardly noticed her; he was transfixed by a pamphlet on the desk in front of him.

Cholera had returned to Britain in August 1853 – striking first in the north-east, as before. By mid-September, it had reached London, and died out again in the winter, but now, in August 1854, it was in full swing again.

John was reading through the 'Weekly Returns' – the latest statistics on births and deaths in London.

'What is it, sir?' Jane enquired after standing in silence for a while. 'What are you so excited about?'

'This, Jane, is what I have been waiting for.' John held up the pamphlet, one corner enthusiastically scrunched up in triumph. 'This could well prove beyond doubt that my ideas are correct.'

'Oh, that sounds encouraging,' was all Jane could think of to say. 'Can I get you anything, sir?' she added after a moment.

'No, thank you.' John's gaze was once again fixed on the document in front of him.

'Very good, sir. Oh, don't forget Dr Richardson is calling at six.' Jane assumed that John had heard her, and she turned and went back downstairs.

Benjamin Richardson was John's best friend – although the two doctors had only met four years before, at the Westminster Medical Society. They were also both members of the new Epidemiological Society, where doctors and scientists discussed epidemiology – the study of epidemics and pandemics.

Even though the last cholera epidemic had died away at the end of 1849, John had not forgotten about the disease. He had given several presentations and he had written to newspapers and journals, trying to promote his ideas and suggesting ways for people to stay cholera-free as this new epidemic took hold. But the main bit of official advice was still to ensure places were well ventilated – to avoid miasma hanging around.

The miasma theory even explained away one of John's best pieces of evidence: the fact that the people living close to the river, near the centre of London, were the most likely to develop cholera. To John, that was because these people were supplied with water taken from the part of the river where sewers emptied their contents – including diarrhoea from cholera victims. There was a correlation between an area's source of water supply and the number of cholera cases there.

But other doctors and scientists saw it differently: people near the centre were also at a lower elevation, only a few metres above sea level. So there was also a correlation between an area's elevation and the number of cholera cases. Assuming miasma was heavier than air, it would be more concentrated the closer you were to sea level. Alternatively, perhaps there was simply more rotting filth at lower levels, which produced more miasma.

One of the most prominent scientists in favour of this interpretation was William Farr, the Registrar General, who wrote the Weekly Returns. Farr was intrigued by John's ideas, but he thought they would be hard to prove.

Benjamin Richardson arrived promptly at six o'clock. 'Jane tells me you have made a breakthrough, John.' Benjamin stood at the door to John's study, his coat over one arm. He was twenty-five years old, John was forty.

'Ah, Benjamin, how was your move?' John enquired, shaking his friend's hand and offering him a seat.

'All good. Now I'm just round the corner, there's no getting rid of me,' Benjamin said with a smile. Left to his own devices, John was not very sociable – but Benjamin often encouraged him to go to dinner parties, and John was always surprised at how much he enjoyed them.

'So, what is this momentous discovery?' Benjamin enquired.

'Well, I've found a way to prove that William Farr's idea about elevation is wrong. In one of the Weekly Returns from last autumn, Farr noted that there are three districts of London where people are supplied with water from two different companies – Lambeth Water and Southwark and Vauxhall Water. In those areas, the pipes of the two companies run side by side. Lambeth Water is supplying water taken from further upstream, away from the polluted parts of the River Thames. Southwark and Vauxhall takes it from near Hungerford Bridge, close to the sewer outlets.'

'And...' Benjamin was beginning to see why John was so excited.

'Well, in those three districts, there are tens of thousands of people – of all ages, a mixture of rich and poor, all living at the same elevation, all breathing the same air, their lives completely intertwined. The only thing that differs among them is the source of their water. People living next door to each other have different water supplies.'

'And what do the statistics say about the cholera deaths in those three areas?' Benjamin asked, anticipating the answer.

'Well, look here,' John said, reaching for another piece of paper. 'I reorganised the information from last autumn's Weekly Returns. Over two months, there were no cholera deaths at all in areas supplied only by Lambeth Water, and one hundred and fourteen cholera deaths per ten thousand people in areas that received water only from Southwark and Vauxhall.

'And look: in those areas where both companies' supplies were intermingled, the death rate from cholera was almost exactly halfway between: sixty deaths per ten thousand people. Now cholera has come back, I wanted to see if the same would be true – and this latest Weekly Return shows that it is! It's perfect.'

'That's marvellous, John,' Benjamin agreed, 'but you know, don't you, that to be certain, you will have to find out exactly which houses had the deaths and which houses get which water?'

'I know, I know. I've been in touch with Mr Farr and, amazingly, he's agreed to get some of his people to do just that. But they can't start for a few weeks, so I'm going to visit some areas, too: walk the streets, and find out who gets what water.'

And so, over the next few weeks, John made hundreds of house-to-house enquiries in the areas where the two water supplies ran side by side; he paid an assistant, Joseph Whiting, to help him.

It was harder than he had thought it would be: many of the houses were rented, and the people living in them had no idea which company supplied their water. John tried to contact the landlords, and when he couldn't do that, he collected a little bit of the water in a bottle, labelled the bottle, and analysed the water back home. He got very good at telling Lambeth water from Southwark and Vauxhall water – often just by sight, sometimes by analysing it with chemicals.

By the end of August 1854, John and Joseph had investigated nearly nine hundred cholera deaths in the areas. In September, when the results from William Farr's researchers were in, too, the conclusion was inescapable. In the mixed areas – where people lived at the same elevation and breathed the same air – those living in houses supplied by Southwark and Vauxhall Water were more than five times as likely to die from cholera than people in houses supplied by Lambeth.

It was a triumph of the scientific method – a fair test. It wasn't just that John felt vindicated: this was really important. If he could prove that his theory was correct, then doctors might be able to develop effective treatments, governments would be able to develop ways of preventing epidemics – and individual people would be able to keep themselves cholera-free by taking simple precautions. This theory might one day save countless lives and mean that people would be spared a painful, tormented and needless death.

While he was still collecting the information about the water companies, something happened that would provide even more striking evidence in support of John's theory, and prove that people got cholera if, and only if, they swallowed the 'cholera poison' that came from another victim's intestines.

9
Outbreak

September 1854

It was Saturday afternoon, 2nd September. John was on his way back from administering chloroform to a three-year-old girl who had needed to have a toe amputated. He often walked to and from his appointments, even when they were several miles away from his home, as this one was. But today, he was keen to get back quickly: he had heard about a sudden increase in cholera cases in Soho, close to his new house, and in the streets around where he used to live. Dozens of people had died in the past couple of days. So he hailed a cab; the driver slowed the horse to a stop at the roadside.

'Where to, sir?' the cab driver enquired, from his seat above and behind the cab.

'Sackville Street, Mayfair, please,' John replied.

'Right-ho. You heard about the terrible goings on near there, sir – in Soho? Dozens of 'em taken by the cholera. They say it's 'cause of them sewer workers diggin' up dead bodies – people what died from the plague.'

John rolled his eyes. 'Yes, I've heard about the cholera outbreak. Although I doubt it's got anything to do with two-hundred-year-old corpses. Besides, the new sewer is some way from where the new cholera cases are – and as far as I know, the workers didn't disturb any of the skeletons. What's more, none of the men digging the sewer have been taken ill.'

'Then what caused it, do you reckon?' the driver asked, his eyes wide open in surprise at such a well-formed response.

'I don't know, but I intend to find out.' John stepped inside the cab, the driver cracked his whip and off they went.

As the cab passed over the River Thames, John glanced down and imagined once again all the cholera poison floating around in the murky water, having been flushed down the city's new sewers.

He felt pleased that his most recent research was adding compelling evidence in favour of his theory – and hopeful that one day water companies would provide clean, safe water for everyone.

John asked the cab driver to stop on Regent Street, halfway between his house and Soho. He had decided to head straight to the heart of the new outbreak and see what he could find out. Two minutes later, he was walking through Golden Square into the heart of the Parish of St James, Soho.

His mind was busy. Taking water from the part of the river polluted with cholera victims' diarrhoea increased the number of cases across a wide area. But in this outbreak in Soho, nearly all the victims lived within a few streets of each other. An intense, localised outbreak like this one had to have a more local, specific cause. He remembered his investigations in Horsleydown and Albion Terrace. *So what might be the cause here?* he wondered.

The part of Soho where the new cholera outbreak was happening, the parish of St James, was a maze of narrow, cobbled streets. One street was much wider than the others – the appropriately-named Broad Street. Normally, it was busy with street sellers and their customers, tradespeople, cows and sheep. But today, things were different.

Many of the residents of St James's had already begun leaving in large numbers, to flee the developing tragedy. Houses and shops were locked and shuttered. Instead of street sellers' handcarts, there were hearses parked here and there, collecting the bodies of those that had died. Along all the streets in St James's, small groups of people clustered around the hearses and followed them from house to house. Many of the people were holding handkerchiefs and scarves over their noses and mouths in the hope of shutting out the miasma they believed was present in the foul-smelling air.

John walked along Broad Street – past the grocers' shops, past the hatters, the tailor and the plumber. And then, as he passed the Eley Brothers factory at 38 Broad Street – which made percussion caps, the explosive part of rifle cartridges – he clapped eyes on what he immediately realised had to be the source of the outbreak.

Just outside number 40 Broad Street, there was a hand pump that was popular with local residents and businesses. People took water from the pump to their homes for cooking and drinking; pubs added it to whisky and other spirits; dining halls served it with food; some shops made fizzy sherbet drinks with it.

The water from the Broad Street pump had a good reputation. And yet, as far as John had heard, nearly all the deaths of the past couple of days were in the immediate area of this pump. If his theory really was correct, and the outbreak was caused by lots of people swallowing cholera poison, then it made sense that it would be in the water – and in such a localised outbreak, the only source of water that fitted the bill was that pump.

On Sunday, John took a little of the water from the Broad Street pump home in a bottle. He examined and tested the water, but he didn't taste it – just in case. The water looked clear and smelt fine – so all Sunday evening he questioned his own conclusion. Perhaps the water from the Broad Street pump *wasn't* the source of the current outbreak.

At his desk, he looked at a map of the area, picturing the streets he knew so well, scanning them like a hawk looking for its prey. There was a slaughterhouse nearby, which people complained about because of the smells that came from the piles of putrid flesh. The area smelt pretty bad generally – especially after this hot August – with hundreds of cesspits and piles of rotting vegetables and dog mess. But John knew that bad smells didn't cause cholera. His eyes kept coming back to that spot on Broad Street where the pump was.

Yes, that pump water had to be the source. He knew what to do: he would have to find out the addresses of everyone that had died, then find out if the victims had been drinking the water from the Broad Street pump in the past few days. He would have to work fast – not only because so many people were dying, but because so many of the living, the people he would actually be able to talk to, were leaving the area.

As he went to bed that evening, John Snow felt a little guilty: he was actually quite excited, while everyone else in the area felt only fear, sadness and despair.

10
Investigation

September 1854

On Monday morning, John had an appointment with a dentist: he had to give chloroform to a patient who was having some teeth extracted. He knew he wouldn't be able to get hold of the addresses of those who had died in the previous week until the next day. And so, when he left the dentist's surgery, he hurried straight back to Soho.

John watched as more bodies were collected; the outbreak had claimed so many victims that street traders' handcarts were being used as makeshift hearses. He watched, too, as more people left town. Then he wandered back to the pump on Broad Street.

'I wouldn't drink that if I were you,' he advised a teenage girl who was collecting a bottleful of the water. As she looked up, he could see that she was sobbing.

'What d'you mean, sir?' the girl sniffed through her tears. 'I'm getting it for my mother. She's sick, sir, with diarrhoea – reckons it's the cholera. She always makes me get water from here. Says it's better than the water from Marlborough Street by where we live. Anyway, why do you say I shouldn't drink it?'

'I think the water from this pump is the source of the cholera outbreak. It's that water that's making people so sick.'

'Get on! It's good water, this.' She pushed the stopper into the bottle and turned, to make her way to deliver the water to her mother.

'Miss – I was wondering: has the water from this pump changed at all over the past week?' John called after her.

'No, sir – not at all. Fresh as ever.' And she continued on her way.

He asked several other people that day about the water – and everyone said it looked and tasted the same as always. But if it was the source of the outbreak, which had begun abruptly only a few days ago, then something in the water must have changed – just something people couldn't see, taste or smell. He decided to take another sample of the water, and study it under his microscope.

Back at home, John placed the bottle on his desk. He felt a chill down his spine as he realised he was almost certainly looking at a killer.

He noticed that after a while, some tiny white flecks settled in the water. There was nothing unusual about that, and apart from those particles, the water was fairly clean. Left to stand for a long time, a thin film formed on the water's surface, which suggested that it contained some sewage – but again, it was nothing very unusual.

Gazing through the lens of his microscope, John could see that the water did contain some cells – he thought back to Swayne and Brittan's 'discoveries' from five years ago – but nothing that looked out of the ordinary.

He was no expert in microscopy, so in the afternoon, he took a sample to his friend, Dr Hassall, who couldn't see anything unusual in the water either. Perhaps the water was now safe, John thought.

On Tuesday morning, John visited the General Register Office, at Somerset House, overlooking the River Thames. He managed to get hold of a list of the addresses of the people who were known to have died of cholera in the week to Saturday 2nd. He sat by the river and read through the list avidly.

Eighty-nine cholera deaths were registered as having taken place in that week in that small part of Soho. Of these, 83 had occurred on the last three days of the week alone: four on the Thursday and 79 on the Friday and Saturday. So John supposed that the outbreak probably began on the Thursday.

Somehow, on the Wednesday or the Thursday, rice-water diarrhoea from someone with cholera must have found its way into the water that supplies the pump. But how? Who? Before he could try to work out the answers to those questions, he had to gather enough evidence to prove that the pump water really was the culprit. There was no time to waste, and he hurried back to Soho to begin visiting the addresses on the list.

When he arrived back in Soho, he saw a small crowd forming. This time, the people were gathered around not a hearse, but a man. John could see that it was the new president of the government's Board of Health, Benjamin Hall.

'... Most important of all is that you do not panic,' Mr Hall was saying. 'Be assured that workers from the Board of Health will be disinfecting all the sources of foul smells in the area, and removing piles of rubbish as we see fit. We have also begun house-to-house visits, to seek out filth and unventilated spaces, in an effort to rid this district of its current outbreak.'

John grimaced, but moved a little closer, so that he could hear better.

'Please also be assured that we have formed a medical council, which will be investigating scientific questions about the disease. The cholera has gripped this area like never before. But we at the Board of Health have the situation under control. We have given advice to the local board of governors, who will be putting our recommendations into practice. We are also keen to stress that there is no need for any more of you to leave the area: once the streets have been washed and the houses ventilated, Soho will be rid of the cause of this outbreak.'

There were cheers from the crowd.

'What should we do, sir?' someone shouted.

'You, as individuals, can do your part to slow the spread of this terrible disease. Do not drink beer or wine in excess. Do not eat food that is going bad. Keep yourself dry. Please make sure that you keep your houses clean and, most importantly, well ventilated.

'And if any of you feel a looseness in your bowels, seek advice from a doctor straight away. The earlier we catch the disease, the more chance there is of saving you.'

Mr Hall leaned forward a little, and some hope glinted in his eyes.

'I can announce that doctors at King's College Hospital have been testing a new cholera treatment, with great success. Rather than try to stop the diarrhoea, they have been encouraging it, by administering half an ounce of castor oil every half hour to, er, ease the diarrhoea's passage. The doctors at the Middlesex Hospital, where the sick from this current outbreak have been taken, are now benefiting from the new treatment.'

John turned away, keen to get on with his detective work. First of all, he worked out that of the 83 deaths from Thursday to Saturday, 73 of the victims' addresses were closer to the Broad Street pump than to any other local pump.

Through the rest of Tuesday, and on Wednesday – while the workers from the Board of Health flushed the street with a pungent solution of chloride of lime, leaving puddles of milky liquid on the cobbles – he went from house to house. He asked whoever he could whether the people who had died from cholera in the past few days had been in the habit of drinking water from the pump on Broad Street.

Nearly every one of them had – and John realised that the people who hadn't actually visited the pump to draw the water could easily have drunk some unknowingly, in coffee shops and restaurants, for example.

He spoke to the owner of a coffee shop, who said she had been serving the water – and she knew of nine of her customers who had died. He spoke to some people who were free of the disease; most of them said they had not recently drunk water from the pump.

On Wednesday evening, John gazed up at the full moon, and reflected on what he had found out. He was certain that the Broad Street pump was the source of the cholera outbreak; and he knew what he would have to do next.

11
A Handle on the Situation

Thursday had been another warm day, but fog filled the evening air as John walked the few streets to the Vestry Hall in Piccadilly, where the Board of Governors of the parish of St James was holding a meeting. John felt nervous – but deep down he also felt strangely confident. He paused at the door to compose himself, took a deep breath, then opened the door and went in.

Inside, the governors were deep in anxious conversation. John stood for a while, waiting for them to surface – waiting for the right moment to introduce himself and say what he had to say.

After a few minutes, he moved closer, gave a little cough, and began to speak.

'I am Doctor Snow. I used to run a practice in Frith Street.'

Some of the governors recognised him. One of them stood and addressed John: 'Good evening, Doctor Snow. We have already enlisted the support of several local doctors, and we are doing all we can to follow the advice of the Board of Health. And, thank God, this abominable cholera outbreak seems to be abating. So if you have come to offer your help, then I am afraid you are too late. We thank you anyway.'

'Ah, no. It is not that,' John replied. 'What I have to say is, of course, related to the cholera outbreak. But I am not offering my help – not exactly. I have a request; something that, I am sure, will strike you as odd. But please, hear me out.'

He scanned the governors' faces, which were looking puzzled. He knew he would have to be succinct but convincing.

'Some years ago, I became convinced that cholera is not caused by foul smells, by miasma, as most scientists and doctors would have you believe. It is my contention that some kind of poison specific to cholera resides in the intestines of those unfortunate people with the disease. The poison somehow multiplies in the intestines, and is flushed out in the rice-water diarrhoea that is so characteristic of this terrible disease. Washed into sewers – or into cesspits, which can overflow into the drains that feed the sewers – the diarrhoea makes its way into water supplies, and other people unknowingly drink the poison.'

John paused for a moment, to make sure he had the governors' attention. It seemed that he did.

'For several years, I have been gathering evidence to test my theory – and every piece of evidence I have found seems to support it. Last week, I endeavoured to find out how so many people in Soho might have swallowed cholera poison.

'I got hold of the names and addresses of everyone who died in the first few days of the outbreak. It seemed that the homes of all the victims were clustered around the pump on Broad Street. I visited the victims' homes and spoke with friends and relatives. Just about every one of those who died had recently drunk water from that pump. And so, I am of the opinion that the Broad Street pump is the source of the outbreak – that somehow, the cholera poison from one person's diarrhoea must have got into the water around the end of August.'

The governors were now more than puzzled; they looked stunned. John continued.

'If you think there is any chance that what I have said might be true, then I implore you to remove the pump's handle as soon as you can.'

At first, there was stunned silence. John sat down. He showed the governors some of his evidence – he had brought a copy of the book he had written in 1849; he had brought the information about the water companies that he'd shown his friend Benjamin; and he had brought a map he had drawn showing where the cholera victims from the past week had lived.

The governors spoke among themselves, then one of them spoke to John.

'Well, it has to be said, your ideas have taken us all by surprise. The water from that pump is very popular, for the simple reason that it seems to be of good quality. And your theory goes against everything we hear from the Board of Health – and from other doctors. But, in consequence of what you have said – and in the light of the evidence you have provided… we agree that it sounds plausible. And we will remove the pump's handle.'

A crowd gathered around the pump on the Friday morning, as the governors began removing the handle. Many of the people were angry, shouting out that this was a ridiculous idea, and a waste of time when there was so much else to do.

The water was almost certainly not dangerous any more; the pump was hardly being used anyway, because so many people had left the area; and the outbreak was already dying away. But this was a momentous event nevertheless – and John felt that his theory was finally being put into practice. This was the sort of action that might one day save lives.

12
Further Investigation

September and October 1854, London

The following week, John visited the General Register Office again, and collected the details of cholera deaths registered up to the 9th September – the second week of the outbreak. Many of the deaths that occurred at the end of the first week had not been registered in time to be included on the first week's list, and were on this second list.

The new details revealed the full extent of the outbreak. It turned out that two hundred people had died in the parish of St James between Thursday 31st August and Saturday 2nd September. And in the first two weeks, there were nearly six hundred cholera deaths altogether.

John was not the only one investigating the terrible cholera outbreak in Soho. A team of people working for the Board of Health was carrying out a detailed survey of the houses in the affected part of Soho, and John crossed paths with them as he continued his own investigation over the next few weeks.

One of the Board of Health's team, a doctor called David Fraser, told John about a man who had come from Brighton to visit his brother in Soho. The brother had been suffering with cholera, but died before the man arrived – so the man only stayed in Soho for a short while. While he was there, he went to lunch in a local restaurant and drank brandy mixed with water – water from the Broad Street pump. On his return to Brighton, he developed cholera and died the next day.

John knew the story was perfectly in line with his theory – but he knew that other people would probably argue that because the man had been in the area, he would have breathed the disease-causing miasma.

Dr Fraser gave John another very important piece of information – something not so easily explained by the miasma theory. Fraser had been studying the list of cholera deaths outside the area, and recognised the name of a woman who had died in leafy Hampstead, a few miles to the north-west. The name was familiar to John, too: it was Susannah Eley, whose sons ran Eley Brothers, the percussion cap factory on Broad Street.

John hurried to the factory.

'Would it be possible to speak to one of the Eley brothers?' John enquired at the entrance to the factory, which was only a few yards from the pump.

Shortly afterwards, a man arrived. 'I am William Eley,' he said.

'Good day, sir. I am John Snow, a doctor. I am carrying out enquiries into the recent outbreak of cholera here in Soho. I was very sorry to hear about the death of your mother. I wonder if I might speak with you about it.'

Mr Eley was looking down at the floor. When he looked up, John could see he had a pained expression as he thought of his mother's death.

'Thank you for your sympathy. What do you want to know?'

'Well, I ...' John paused as he realised that the pump he was about to accuse as Susannah Eley's killer was in view. 'I was wondering if your mother was in Soho at the time of the outbreak – and in particular, whether she drank the water from that pump.' John motioned with his eyes.

'No. My mother hasn't – hadn't – been to Soho for some time. But the pump? She liked the water very much, and since a cart used to travel most days from here to her home in Hampstead, we always used to send a bottle of it to her.'

'Did you ... send some water to her around the beginning of September?' John asked, aware that now he was not only accusing the pump. He was also accusing Mr Eley himself of unwittingly being responsible for his own mother's death.

'Yes, we did,' was the response.

John did not press him any further about his mother. But he did ask more about the pump water. He knew that out of fewer than two hundred people working at the factory, eighteen had died of cholera in the recent outbreak.

'Do your workers take the water?' His eyes flicked once again in the direction of the pump.

'Yes, we keep two large tubs of it in the factory, and most of our workers drink it.'

After leaving the Eley Brothers' factory, John passed Huggins and Company, the brewery on the same street, which was offering hot water night and day for people to use to clean their houses. From the information supplied by the General Register Office, he knew that there had been no deaths at all among the brewery workers.

Mr Huggins confirmed that none of his seventy or so workers had died, although two had had a mild case of diarrhoea. He also told John that the brewery had its own well and a water supply, and that as far as he knew, his workers almost never drank the water from the pump.

As he continued his investigation, John uncovered other cases in which people had been spared from cholera because they had not drunk the Broad Street pump water.

The most striking was the workhouse on Poland Street, only about a hundred metres from the Broad Street pump. The workhouse was home to more than five hundred people too poor or too sick to support themselves – the residents were given needlework and other menial jobs to do. John estimated that if cholera had struck there with the same ferocity it had in the rest of the neighbourhood – as the miasma theory would suggest it should have – then more than fifty people would have died. But there were only five deaths. It turned out that the workhouse had its own water supply, and the residents hardly ever drank water from the Broad Street pump.

Everything seemed to be going John's way. With what he had found out here, and the information about the water companies – along with all the other evidence he had collected in the previous few years – there would be enough to write another, longer book to set out his theory. Perhaps now the world would take him more seriously.

13
Inquiry

1854 – 1855, London

In November 1854, while John was writing his new book, officials from the local parish decided to set up their own inquiry into the September outbreak. John was invited onto the parish's Cholera Inquiry Committee. As part of their inquiry, the committee asked the government organisation in charge of the roads – the Paving Board – to investigate the well beneath the Broad Street pump. John was thrilled – was absolute proof of his theory about to be uncovered?

One of the other people on the committee was a local clergyman called Henry Whitehead, who had worked as hard as John had to investigate the September outbreak, and who had written a pamphlet describing what he had found out. As a clergyman, Whitehead had been confronted with the horror of the cholera deaths, having sat at the bedsides of many of the dying during the outbreak.

When Whitehead had heard of John's theory, in September, he had not believed it – and had privately decided it would be easy to disprove it. Now the two were working together on the committee.

'I would be surprised if the Paving Board finds anything in that well,' Whitehead goaded John at one of the committee meetings. 'If your theory is correct, and cholera poison from victims' diarrhoea has been getting into the well water, then it must have come from the sewer that passes nearby. But if that was happening, then surely the outbreak would have spread and become still worse –'

He paused for effect.

'– because the five hundred or so newly-infected people would have produced yet more of the poison, which would have ended up in the sewer – then in the well – and it would have infected still more people. But the outbreak didn't get worse, did it? After the first few days, there were fewer new cases, not more – and the outbreak was over within a couple of weeks.'

John couldn't really respond to Whitehead's criticism – but he felt assured that the answer would lie under the ground, beneath the pump. The well was opened on 27th November. Mr Farrell, who worked for the Paving Board, explained to John what was – and wasn't – found:

'Well, John. We have opened the well and conducted a thorough investigation,' Mr Farrell began. 'I know this is probably not what you want to hear... but the brick lining of the well appears intact and water-tight. We couldn't find any way that sewage could get into the water.'

John was disappointed – but he was undeterred, and he was still sure that the source of the outbreak had to be that water in the well beneath the pump.

At the beginning of December, he went to a meeting of the Epidemiological Society. He took along a map he had made, and set it out on a table for everyone to see.

'On the map, I have marked all the houses where the victims of the outbreak lived,' John explained to a small group of the Society's members, 'and as you can see, they are all clustered around this point – the location of the pump on Broad Street.'

Everyone thought it was a stunning visual representation of the outbreak, and that it did seem to point to the pump as the source of the problem. Of course, that didn't mean they agreed with his ideas.

Although the committee was still investigating the recent outbreak, John pushed on with the writing of his new book. This second version was much longer and more detailed than the first. John added all the evidence he had gathered since 1849 and, of course, he went into great detail about what he had found in Soho.

He included a copy of the map he had presented at the Epidemiological Society – but he added an important feature: a dotted line that encircled the pump. From any point inside the line, the Broad Street pump was closest; outside the line, other local pumps were closer. The line wasn't a circle, because of the way the streets were laid out and because of the locations of the other pumps.

The line made the case against the pump even clearer: nearly all the cholera deaths of the outbreak were at addresses inside the dotted line. And of those people who had died of cholera but whose homes were outside the dotted line, John knew that most of them had drunk the water from the Broad Street pump.

John finished the book in December. He gave this new version the same title as the first – *On The Mode of Communication of Cholera* – but he added *Second Edition, much Enlarged*. Knowing that most doctors and scientists would probably still not believe him, he wrote a sarcastic comment at the beginning of the book:

I feel every confidence that my present labours will receive the same kind consideration from the medical profession which has been accorded to my former endeavours to ascertain the causes of cholera.

The book was published in January, and John sent a copy to Henry Whitehead, who remained unconvinced... at first.

Part of Whitehead's role in the inquiry was to make door-to-door visits to gather as much information as he could – about the people who had died and those who had survived. While John had mostly concentrated on the drinking habits of those who had suffered from cholera, Whitehead was keen to find out if those who had *not* caught the disease had also drunk water from the Broad Street pump. He guessed that the use of the Broad Street pump would be as common among the survivors as John had found it to be among the victims. If that were true, then John's evidence would be meaningless – and worthless.

At the end of March 1855, Whitehead saw John walking through Soho.

'John!' he called out. 'I must speak with you.'

14
Nappies

John stopped and faced Whitehead. A warm spring breeze danced on his face, the sound of horses' hooves and cartwheels on the busy street filled his ears, and a picture of a smiling, enthusiastic clergyman filled his eyes. He wondered why Whitehead might be so keen to speak to him.

'Ah, Henry. How are you?' he said.

'I'm well, thank you. Listen: I have finished my investigations. I've gathered information about five hundred of the people who were living in Broad Street at the time of the outbreak. And you will be amazed – but perhaps not surprised – at what I have found.'

John was intrigued – questions buzzed around his head – but Whitehead continued excitedly before he could ask him anything.

'There are two hundred and ninety-nine of the residents of Broad Street who I know didn't drink the water from the pump in that fateful week at the beginning of September. Of those people, only twenty developed cholera – that's fewer than seven per cent; about one in fifteen. But I know of one hundred and forty or so residents who *did* drink the water – and of them, at least eighty developed the disease. John, that's nearly sixty per cent – more than half!'

John was thrilled.

'John – you were right all along. And here, surely, is enough proof to convince anyone. I can't believe I couldn't see it before. I'm sorry.'

John felt as if his heart was leaping up and down with pride inside his chest. Finally, someone else understood cholera as he did.

'But wait. There's something else,' Whitehead went on. 'There was a case that I had overlooked, which I have come to think might be the one that started it all off. It was a girl of five months old; she died on the second of September, just a couple of days after the outbreak began. And John – I have been to speak the girl's poor mother.'

'And?' John was quivering with tension.

'The mother told me that the girl had been ill for several days. She said that she had washed the girl's soiled nappies in a bucket, and poured the bucket's contents into a cesspool near the front of her house. And where do you think she lived?'

John knew that Whitehead was about to tell him that the girl had lived close to the pump – but just how close came as a welcome surprise.

'John, she lived at number forty Broad Street – right next to the pump! I have asked that a surveyor be allowed to investigate the drains and the cesspool, to see if there is any way the diarrhoea from the soiled nappies could have passed into the well.'

Just a few weeks later, a surveyor inspected number 40 Broad Street. A drain inside the building was supposed to empty waste water and sewage into the new sewer, but the drain was old and the bricks in its lining could be lifted out easily; the cement between the bricks had decayed. Along the length of the drain, there was a brick-built tank

– a cesspool that was designed to prevent smells coming back up into the house. But it was blocked and overflowing.

The surveyor emptied it, and found that the bricks that lined it were in as bad a state as the bricks in the lining of the drain. The waste water from the cesspool was leaking out into the soil and gravel around it. And the wall of the cesspool was less than three feet away from the brick wall of the well.

When the Paving Board had inspected the well months before, the brick lining had appeared intact. But looking from the other side, from outside the well, the surveyor could see that waste water from the cesspool at number 40 had been leaking through the lining and into the well.

He dug out the ground between the cesspool and the well, just to make sure; the soil was black and swampy. Bricks were removed from the well lining, and there was evidence that sewage from number 40 had definitely seeped into the well.

On 25th July 1855, the Cholera Inquiry Committee finished its report on the outbreak in Soho. The report concluded that the cholera outbreak was 'in some manner' due to the impure water of the well in Broad Street.

Officially, the committee didn't go as far as supporting John's theory – but it didn't disagree with it, either. To John, after so many years of rejection, that felt like a triumph.

15
Afterwards

John Snow only lived for another three years after the committee's report. During those last years, he continued working as a doctor and an anaesthetist, and he administered chloroform to Queen Victoria again, during the birth of her ninth child. And, of course, he carried on promoting his theory in lectures and medical journals. But despite all the compelling evidence, there were still only a few people who believed it could actually be true.

When he died from a stroke in 1858 – at the age of just 45 – fewer than sixty copies of his 1855 book had been sold. He had spent £200 having it printed (equivalent to around £15,000 today), but he made only a few pounds from it. The money didn't matter – he would have given all the copies of the book away free if he thought his message would get through.

Henry Whitehead became a champion of John's cause. When another cholera epidemic was beginning in Britain in 1866, Whitehead publicised John's theory, and searched for evidence to support it – as John had done for all those years.

Gradually, scientists and doctors began to understand that living things – germs – cause most diseases, and not bad smells. And gradually, more people began to accept what John had realised long before: cholera really is a disease you get from swallowing something that has come from a cholera victim's intestines.

The world began to realise that John Snow was actually something of a hero. Today, people often refer to him as the founder of modern epidemiology, the study of the spread and control of diseases.

If you are ever in Soho, in central London, you can visit a replica water pump that has been placed near to where the original one stood. Broad Street still exists, but today it is called Broadwick Street. Nearby is a pub named after John Snow.

What John didn't know was that in December 1854, while John was putting the finishing touches to his book, the Italian scientist Filippo Pacini had identified the cholera poison. Pacini had found a particular type of bacterium in abundance in the rice-water diarrhoea of cholera victims – and in the intestines of people who had died from the disease. John's friend, the microscopist Arthur Hassall, also spotted these strange, comma-shaped bacteria in diarrhoea from cholera patients when he was working for the Board of Health. But Hassall believed that the bacteria were a consequence, and not the cause, of cholera.

Pacini's discovery went unnoticed. But in 1883, another pioneering scientist and a better-known one, the German microbiologist Robert Koch, identified exactly the same species of bacterium. He named it *Vibrio cholerae* and proved conclusively that it was the cause of cholera.

John probably realised that the world would one day catch up with him. If he ever looked far ahead into the future, he would doubtless have guessed that cholera would be completely absent in the twenty-first century.

It is not. Despite the fact that the disease is easy to prevent and easy to treat, hundreds of thousands of cholera cases, and several thousand cholera deaths, are reported each year. And reported cases are just the tip of the iceberg. The best estimates of the total number of cases, including those unreported, put the number of cases at two or three million a year, and the number of deaths at more than one hundred thousand.

Nearly all the cases of cholera in the modern world are in poor countries, where people do not have a clean, safe water supply – something that John Snow realised is vital to public health.